SCHOLASTIC

Let's Find Out

My REBUS Reader

I0890035

Where Can You Find Friends?

by Amanda Miller

SCHOLASTIC INC.

New York Toronto London Auckland Sydney New Delhi Hong Kong

You can find friends at the  .

computer

You can find friends on the  .

rug

You can find friends on the .

bus

You can find friends on the .

swings

You can find friends in the  .

library

You can find friends at the  .

sink

You can find friends at  !

school

Read it again! Find th
hidden pencil on eac
page.